So, You Want To Be A
PRINCESS?

Written By Janet Gilman Olson

Illustrated By Elizabeth Craddock

For my mom,

Olympia, who taught me

that girls can indeed

do anything.

Yippee! You were born a **GIRL!**
There's so much girls can do,
but to walk around with a crown
just might limit you.

You can be a **TEACHER**

who teaches cows to speak.

Or monkeys to sing Opera,

or snails to take a leap!

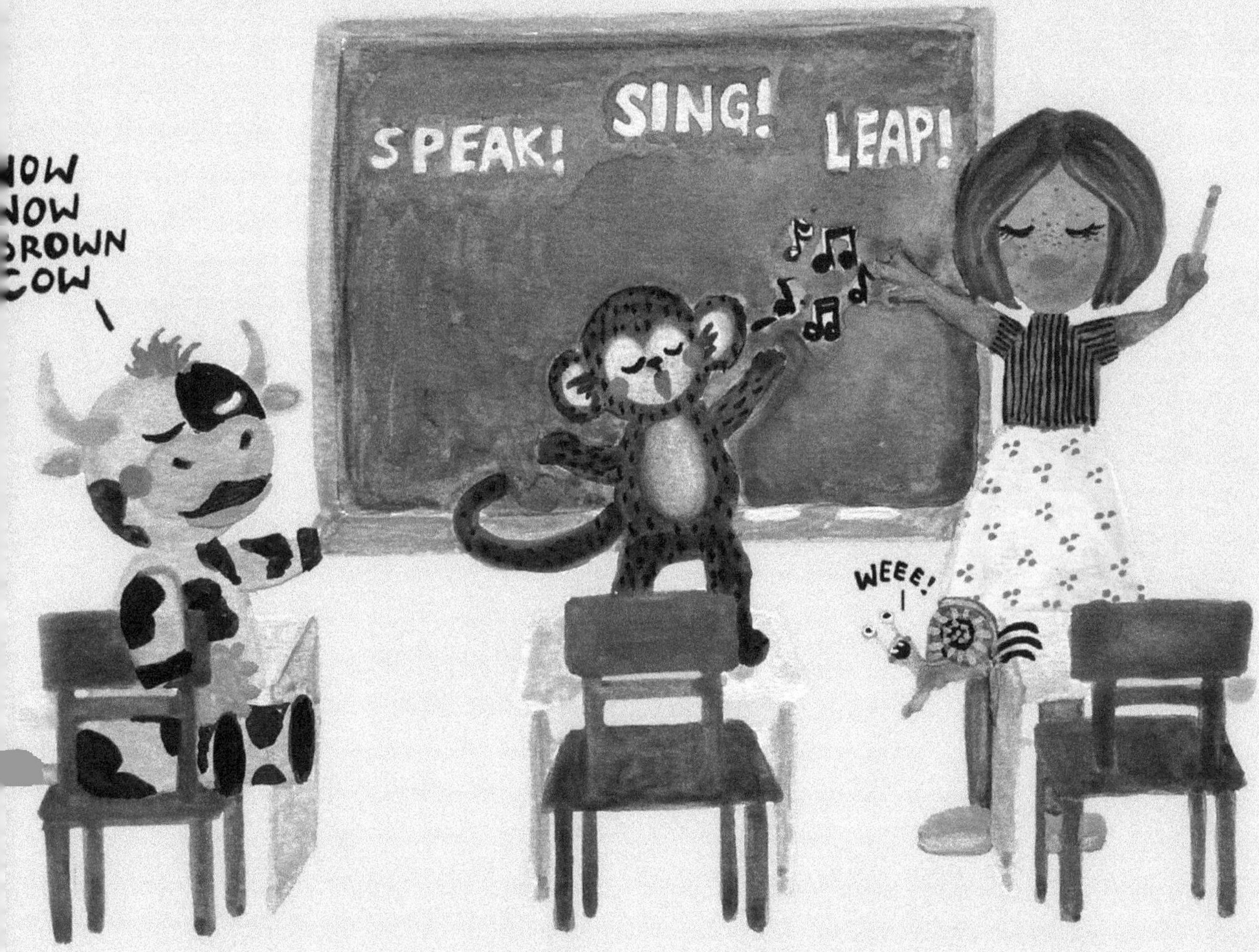
SPEAK!
SING!
LEAP!
WEEE!

You can be a **SCIENTIST**
who finds a complex cure
for germs that makes bears curtsy
or Spanish bulls demure.

You can be a **THERAPIST** who works on side-lined llamas who got their wobbly kneecaps from their long-necked mamas.

You can be a **DANCER**
who trains giraffes to jig,
who makes her Broadway debut
pirouetting with a pig.

You can be an **ARCHITECT**
designing homes for cats
with scratching posts in every room
and hooks for all their hats.

You can be a **DRAG RACER**

in a sequined purple car.

The guy who came in second

says you're the best - by FAR!

You can be a **PARTY HOST**
for a penguin's birthday bash,
where the meerkats will dance wildly
and the otters make a splash.

You can be a **MUSICIAN**
performing on a stage.
All the kids at school will say
your music's all the rage.

You can be an **ASTRONAUT**
discovering beings unknown
in a polka-dotted galaxy
where no one else has flown.

You can be a **DOCTOR**
healing helpless hippos
and weakened weary wombats
or other hairy sickos.

You can be a **DENTIST**
for a panda's pearly whites,
and a monkey's whiskered mandibles,
or a pony's overbite.

You can be a **PHYSICIST**

who studies energy.

The doctor who sits next to you

might be a *chimpanzee*.

You can be an **ARTIST**

painting family pictures

of elephant reunions

or baby boa constrictors.

You can be a **CEO**
of the world's best company
making itsy-bitsy mittens
for baby bumblebees.

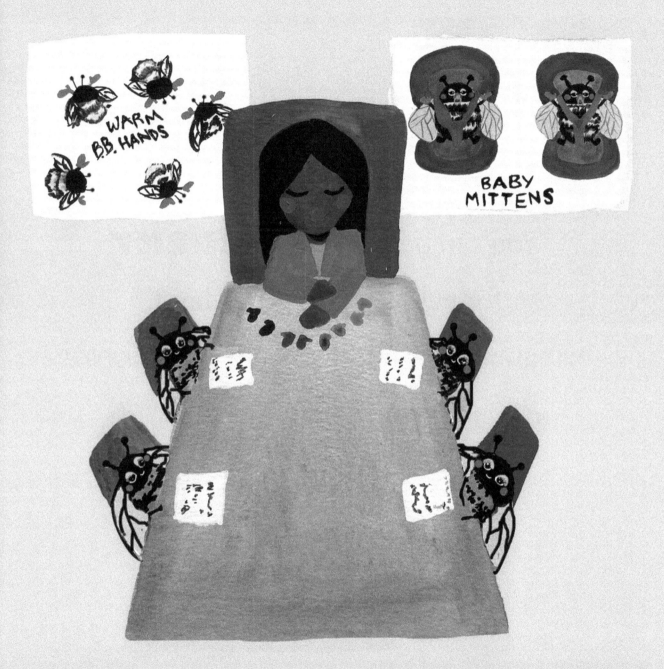

You can be the **PRESIDENT**
for people across your land,
bringing peace and truth and righteousness
and to all a helping hand.

As a **GIRL,** you're awfully cool,

your talent's off the charts.

You'll accomplish EVERYTHING

if you really use your smarts.

The whole wide world is better off
with **WOMEN IN THE LEAD**
and it starts at home, with girls like you
who help where there's a *need*.

While princesses are fair enough,
the world **NEEDS** can-do daughters
who know that they will change the world
when their dreams are fostered.

I CAN EXPLORE! I CAN CREATE! I CAN SPEAK UP! I CAN BE BRAVE!

Now close your eyes and dream

REAL BIG.

What do you want to achieve?

The sky's the limit for girls like you

If only you believe.

About the Author:

Janet Gilman Olson is a western WA native who lives in

Snoqualmie WA with her husband, son and their two rescue pups.

She enjoys kayaking, mountain biking and being outdoors.

She writing her second children's book.

About the Illustrator:

Elizabeth Craddock is from Tacoma, WA and lives in Seattle, WA.

She loves spending time with friends and family, painting with

watercolor and going on picnics. She is illustrating her third book and

expanding her creative career.

CPSIA information can be obtained
at www.ICGtesting.com
Printed in the USA
BVHW061923040122
625449BV00005B/309